Ecosystem
Adventures

Mc Graw Hill Wright Group

The *McGraw·Hill* Companies

www.WrightGroup.com

 **Wright Group**

Send all inquiries to:
Wright Group/McGraw-Hill
P.O. Box 812960
Chicago, IL 60681

ISBN 978-0-07-656417-0
MHID 0-07-656417-7

6 7 8 9 DOC 16 15 14 13 12 11

The **McGraw·Hill** Companies

Contents

How are living things connected?

Just what are ecosystems? And where do you find them? **Ecosystems** are everywhere. They are all alike and they are all different. How can that be? Each one has living and nonliving things, and each ecosystem is special. You might be surprised to learn how the parts of an ecosystem fit together and how each part helps keep the ecosystem in balance.

Focus Questions

What roles do the parts of an ecosystem play?

Why do living things need each other?

What happens when there are changes to an ecosystem?

How do people play a part in ecosystems?

 Preview ▶   online coach

What roles do the parts of an ecosystem play? Preview pages 6–27. Then read *Tropical Rain Forests* to find out.

5

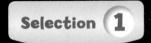

Tropical Rain Forests

LEVELS OF LIFE

by Jeanne Baca Schulte

CHAPTER 1
Where in the World?

What kind of ecosystem do you live in? Do you live in a hot desert or a forest? Maybe you live in a frozen tundra or a grassland. Wherever you live, you are part of an ecosystem.

You are about to explore a rain forest ecosystem. Before we take a closer look, let's learn more about ecosystems. All healthy ecosystems are different, but they all work the same way. They are made up of living and nonliving parts that all work together.

The nonliving parts of an ecosystem are the sun, soil, water, air, and rocks. Things that were once alive also form parts of the ecosystem. There is balance in an ecosystem. Living plants and animals need just the right amount of nonliving things to grow.

soil: dirt

A healthy tropical rain forest has a lot of plant life.

The living things in an ecosystem are the plants and animals. Even you are a living thing in an ecosystem. Living things need one another to **survive**. This is called **interdependence**. If one thing becomes different in an ecosystem, the balance changes.

Climate is an important part of an ecosystem. Climate is the weather in an area over a long time. It includes the temperature, the wind, and the amount of **precipitation**, or water, a place gets. Animals and plants in different ecosystems need different amounts of water and sun. That's why each ecosystem is very special.

In some rain forests, there is heavy precipitation all year long. In others, there is precipitation only during certain seasons.

Strategy Tool Kit
Make Inferences
Why do you think plants and animals need each other to survive?

Measuring Precipitation

The amount of precipitation an area gets is part of its climate. Look at the chart below. How is the Amazon Rain Forest's precipitation in August different from its precipitation in January?

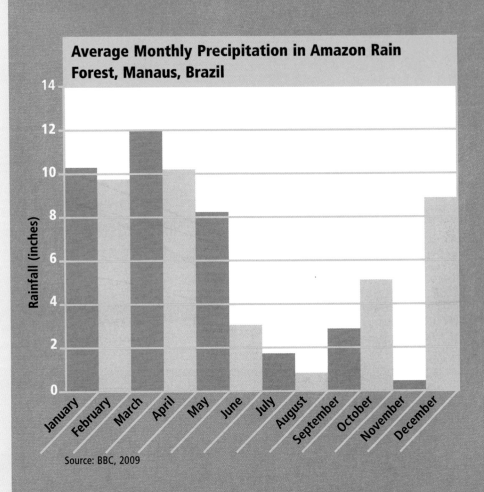

Average Monthly Precipitation in Amazon Rain Forest, Manaus, Brazil

Source: BBC, 2009

CHAPTER 2
Welcome to the Tropical Rain Forest!

Picture a tropical rain forest around you. Can you hear the birds chirping and the monkeys howling? Do you see the monkeys scampering from branch to branch high above? Can you see the tall trees with their hanging vines? Can you see the bright flowers fluttering high above? Can you see any insects in the air, on the plants, or on the ground?

You are walking on the rain forest floor, and it is shady. The floor only gets from about two to fifteen percent of the sunlight from above. The air is very <u>damp</u> and you feel very warm.

> **damp:** wet

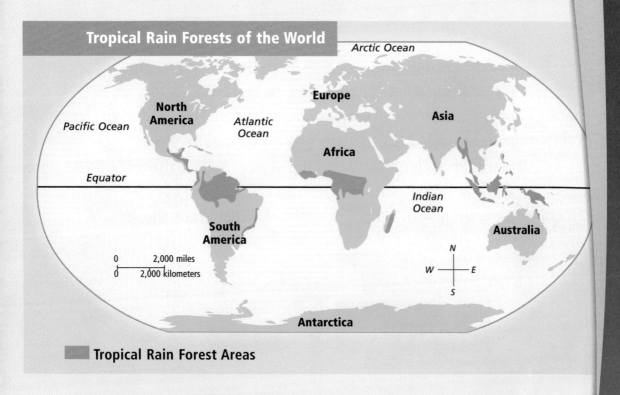

Tropical Rain Forests of the World

Arctic Ocean

Europe

North America

Asia

Pacific Ocean

Atlantic Ocean

Africa

Equator

Indian Ocean

South America

Australia

0   2,000 miles
0   2,000 kilometers

N
W — E
S

Antarctica

Tropical Rain Forest Areas

Look at the map. Tropical rain forests are only found in places near the Equator. These places get twelve hours of sunlight each day. The temperature stays warm all year long, and it also rains a lot. The thousands of plants and animals need the warm and **moist** air to live and grow.

Strategy Tool Kit
Summarize

What are tropical rain forests like?

The tropical rain forest ecosystem is like an apartment building with four **distinct** stories. The forest floor is like the first story. It is very shady, so only shade-loving plants can live there. The second story is called the understory, and it has big-leaf plants that flourish with little sunlight. The third story is called the **canopy**. The trees of the canopy get a lot of sun. They grow much taller than the

Rain Forest Structure

EMERGENT LAYER

CANOPY

UNDERSTORY

FLOOR

plants in the understory. The fourth and last story is called the emergent layer. The tallest trees in the rain forest are in the emergent layer.

Different plants and animals live on each story. To find food and water, the animals may move up or down from story to story. But just as you sleep in your own bed each night, the animals always go home to their own story to sleep.

The Forest Floor

Few plants can live on the floor of the rain forest because there is too little light. But decomposers can live there. Snails, worms, termites, and other small animals are decomposers. Even smaller decomposers are bacteria and fungi.

Decomposers get their food from leaves, animal waste, and dead animals. They break up whatever is left from a living thing into tiny bits. The tiny bits make the soil rich and help it hold water.

Fungi are decomposers. They look like plants, but they do not make their own food.

Many food chains begin on the rain forest floor. Food chains describe how energy is passed from one thing to another. Food webs show how food chains fit together.

Most food chains start with plants. Plants are producers. Producers do not need living things to get their energy. They make their own food using sunlight.

All animals are consumers, which means they eat living or dead things. There are three kinds of consumers. Herbivores, such as beetles, eat only plants. Carnivores, such as some birds, eat only animals. Omnivores, such as iguanas, eat both plants and animals.

Tropical Rain Forest Food Web

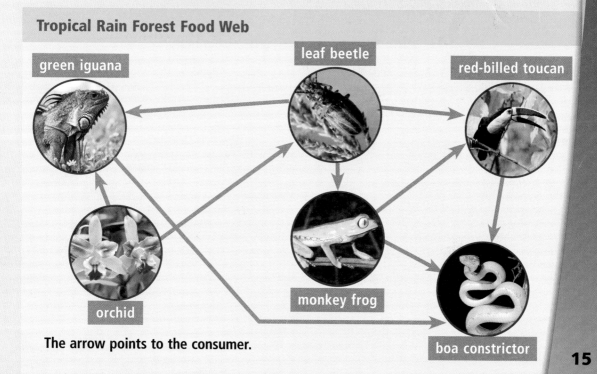

green iguana

leaf beetle

red-billed toucan

orchid

monkey frog

boa constrictor

The arrow points to the consumer.

The Understory

Grab a vine and swing through the understory! The understory gets more sun than the forest floor, but it is still shady. The trees are thin and straight. They have little chance to grow tall, because they get so little light. They are only 15 to 20 feet high. Their leaves are flat and large because they need to **absorb** as much sunlight as they can!

The understory is a great place for animals to hide and a good place for predators to hunt. Animals such as monkeys, apes, and birds eat the flowers, fruits, and nuts that grow in the understory trees. Snakes come down from the canopy to snatch a bird or lizard. What a tasty lunch!

If a tall tree from the canopy falls, the sunlight can reach the ground. Then a seed on the ground will quickly grow into another tall tree. It will grow toward the light until it towers over the understory.

A Closer Look

Race to the Sun
Many rain forest trees wait a long time to grow. But when they do grow, watch out! If a storm, fire, or falling branch makes a small hole in the canopy, the tree will suddenly grow toward the light as fast as it can.

Orangutans eat fruit, leaves, and insects that they find in the understory.

Stop and Think

What kinds of plants and animals have you learned about so far? Where can you find them in the rain forest?

The Canopy

Trees in the canopy can grow more than 100 feet tall. There are many leaves that shade the animals and help them hide.

More plants and animals live here than anywhere else in the tropical rain forest. Between 70 and 90 percent of all rain forest life is here. There are lots of bewildering "mini ecosystems" in the canopy. Some of them you have to see to believe!

A howler monkey howls from the top of a tree.

This three-toed sloth hangs from the branch of a rain forest tree.

One animal that lives in the canopy is the three-toed sloth. It lives in the Amazon rain forest. The sloth has a whole ecosystem in its fur! Small green plants called algae grow in its hairs. Insects also live in the sloth's fur, and they eat the algae that grow alongside them.

When the sloth comes down from the canopy to leave its waste, the insects jump off the sloth to lay their eggs in the dung. The insects hop back on before the sloth goes up the tree. The eggs hatch, and the new insects jump onto a new sloth.

Plants often grow high up on the trunks and branches of the canopy trees. How did the plants get there? The animals took them, of course! Many animals get around by jumping, flying, or gliding. The animals shake canopy tree leaves loose, and the leaves fall into small cracks and pockets on the tree branches. Animals leave their waste on the trees too. The waste and the fallen leaves eventually help new growths begin.

Plants of the Tropical Rain Forest

Birds and small mammals use the ferns in the rain forest as nests.

Many amphibians, such as frogs, lay their eggs on moss that hangs over water.

fern

moss

Plants help animals survive too. One example is the bromeliad plant, a plant whose leaves can hold a lot of water. Insects live in the water and lay their eggs in the plant.

The poison arrow frog uses the water in the bromeliad for her tadpoles. First she lays eggs on the forest floor. The tadpoles hatch and the frog mother takes them up to the plant. The tadpoles eat the insects and eggs in the water, and soon they grow into frogs.

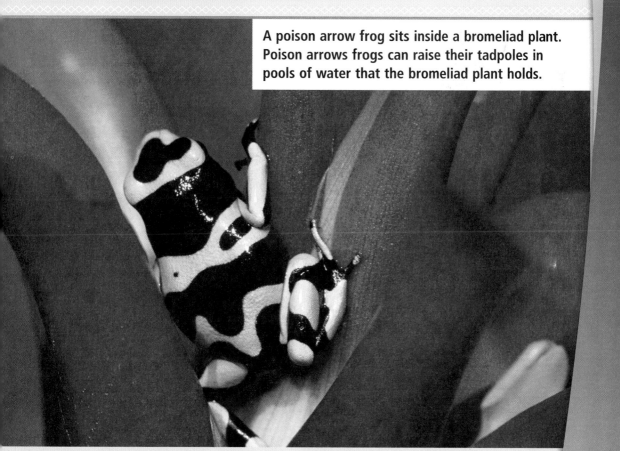

A poison arrow frog sits inside a bromeliad plant. Poison arrows frogs can raise their tadpoles in pools of water that the bromeliad plant holds.

The Emergent Layer

Now climb up to the emergent layer, the highest level of the tropical rain forest. It is mostly home to tall trees and vines. The trees here can reach more than 200 feet high. Rain forest vines can grow up to 3,000 feet in length.

It is very windy in the emergent layer. The wind helps seeds travel so plants and trees can grow in new places.

Clouds of mist fall on the emergent layer of the rain forest.

Not as many animals live in the emergent trees. Some birds like macaws, toucans, and eagles build their nests here. You can find butterflies here too. Some fruit bats and monkeys also live here.

The harpy eagle is one type of bird that lives in the emergent tree tops. It has **terrific** eyesight which makes it a powerful hunter. The eagle perches and looks down into the rain forest for a long time. When it sees a bird, small monkey, or young sloth, it dives down and gets food.

Did You Know?

A Fast Flyer
The harpy eagle can fly as fast as 50 miles per hour, even through the trees.

Strategy Tool Kit
Make Inferences
Why do you think not as many animals live in the emergent layer?

CHAPTER 3
The Night World

The world of the tropical rain forest **transforms** when night falls. Now the sounds of insects and frogs fill the forest. Fruit bats screech. Snakes slither and rodents rustle along the forest floor.

Some animals, such as small reptiles and frogs, are nocturnal. Nocturnal animals come out at night to find food. It is too dangerous for them to come out during the day. If they did, the birds would see them and eat them.

> **rodents:** small animals

A python looks down in the darkness. Pythons hunt small animals, such as rodents, birds, and lizards.

Other animals, such as owls and pythons, come out at night because it is easier for them to find food. Pythons have a special heat sensor that helps them hunt their prey. A warm animal is easier for them to find in the cooler night. Owls hunt at night when most birds are asleep. They use their keen hearing to find prey.

Because it has such good hearing and eyesight, this lesser sooty owl can search for food at night.

Plants need to spread their pollen. Plants use pollen to make fruit or flowers. During the day, bees take pollen from plant to plant. Hummingbirds sip nectar, or sweet liquid, from flowers. Then pollen rubs off on their feathers. When the hummingbirds fly to another flower, the pollen falls onto the flower. At night, bats help spread the pollen. They have a strong sense of smell, which makes it easier to find plants. Some plants even help the bats find them by putting out a special smell.

Some plants only **bloom** at night. Other living things, like some types of fungi, contain tissues that cause them to glow in the dark.

> pollen: plant powder

Some fungi bloom at night and glow in the dark.

Strategy Tool Kit
Visualize
What do you think the rain forest looks like when it is dark?

Sum It Up

Rain forests cover about six percent of the land on Earth. More than 50 percent of the plant and animal species in the world can be found here. Many of the species have not even been named yet! All the parts of a rain forest must work together for the plants and animals to survive. Plants need animals to spread their seeds and pollen. Animals need plants for food. Plants can also protect animals from predators. Everything is connected. Changing any part of the ecosystem may hurt the rest of the rain forest.

Think Back
Selection 1

Focus Question: What roles do the parts of an ecosystem play?

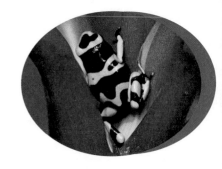

A Check Understanding ★

Make a list of some living and nonliving things found in a tropical rain forest. What roles do these things play in the tropical rain forest ecosystem? PRACTICE COMPANION **109**

B Understand Text Features ★★

Look at the diagram on page 15. How does it help you understand more about the selection?

Discuss the diagram with your partner. Explain what information the diagram adds to the selection.

C Share and Compare ★★

Create a Venn diagram with a partner that shows the similarities and differences between the ecosystems in each of your selections. Which things are the same and why? Which things are different and why?

D Think Critically ★★★★

How are living things connected? Use examples from your selection to explain.

My Home Page

Selection Connection

In *Tropical Rain Forests: Levels of Life* you learned about the rain forest ecosystem. *Coyote's Desert Day* is a fiction selection. You will learn how living things in the desert need each other.

Show What You Know

Think about the following living things: *birds*, *plants*, and *caterpillars*. Why might they need each other?

Write your ideas.

PRACTICE COMPANION **110**

Preview

Why do living things need each other? Preview pages 30–53. Then read *Coyote's Desert Day* to find out.

29

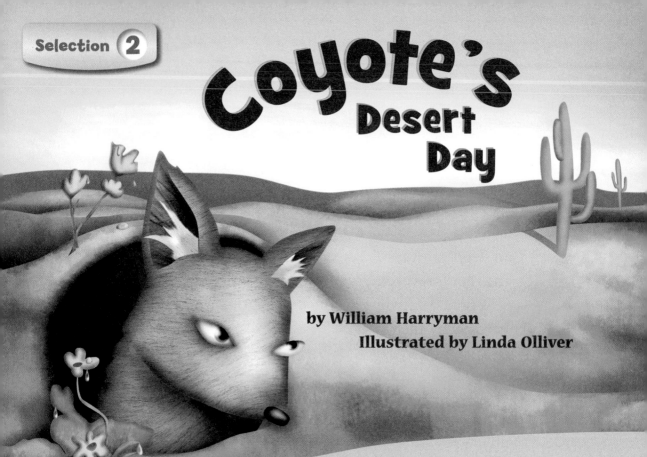

Coyote's Desert Day

by William Harryman

Illustrated by Linda Olliver

CHAPTER 1

Coyote's Wet Morning

Coyote spent all night in her den, trying to stay out of the rain. "I hate the rain," she whined. "I wish I did not have to leave my dry and warm den, but I am too hungry to stay here and wait!"

The rain finally stopped, and the rising sun slowly warmed the wet desert. Coyote looked outside at the canyon around her and saw that the ground was starting to dry.

She slowly **stumbled** out of her den. She was very, very hungry, and it was time to find food.

Finding food would not be easy because Coyote was not the best hunter, and it seemed like she was always making mistakes. Because Coyote was so young, she was still very **clumsy**!

Coyote's stomach was growling, and all she could think about was filling it. When she tried to eat a prickly pear fruit, she yelped.

"Aaaiiieee!" The needles on the prickly pear hurt her tongue. *I want some meat*, she thought. *I need to catch something, fast!*

canyon: narrow valley

31

There were many animals in the desert after three days of rain. Coyote felt excited as she looked around. Pronghorns, rabbits, ground squirrels, and birds were all out searching for food. Her stomach rumbled again, and her mouth watered.

This was the first spring that Coyote had been away from her mother. Her mother was a very good hunter. Coyote was just a year old, but she was fully grown and learning her part in the world. Her mother had new pups to take care of, so Coyote would have to hunt alone.

She crept across the desert, trying to find prey. Then she remembered something her mother once told her. "Do not hunt the mule deer until you are older," she instructed. "They are big and strong, and you might get hurt."

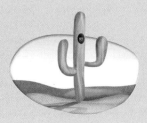

CHAPTER 2

A Search in the Desert

Coyote walked through the low brush and a branch slapped her on the nose. As she moved away from it, she noticed a lizard sunning itself. The lizard did not see her. It lay still, and then snapped its tongue to catch a grasshopper that hopped by. Coyote watched the lizard chew on its meal. *What would her mother do to catch the tiny lizard?*

Even though the lizard was small, Coyote knew it would taste good and be worth the hunt. She lowered herself to the ground to hide from the lizard. She slowly inched toward the meal, while the lizard just kept on eating. Then, with one sudden movement, she <u>pounced</u> on the lizard before it could escape.

pounced: jumped

Coyote clamped her sharp teeth around the lizard's tail. *That was easy,* thought Coyote. *What a great hunter I am.* Then the lizard's tail suddenly broke off and the lizard ran away.

Yum! Coyote swallowed the tail. The tail was a nice snack, but it wasn't enough to fill her empty belly. Coyote's stomach rumbled again. *It's just as well,* she thought. *A lizard is too small a meal for me.*

So Coyote began walking again until she came to a wash where the brush was thinner. During the summer **monsoons**, the washes filled with rainwater. Even though it had rained a lot the night before, there was only a small stream in the wash now. It would be a great place to look for food.

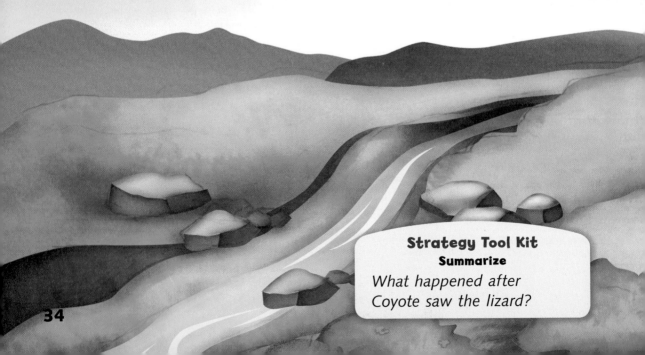

Strategy Tool Kit
Summarize
What happened after Coyote saw the lizard?

Suddenly, Coyote smelled something <u>delicious</u>.
Her mouth began to water, and her stomach rumbled
loudly once again. *A rabbit!* she thought. *At last, I can
get something to fill my empty stomach!*

Coyote stood very still and looked around. A
sudden noise would scare the rabbit. She sniffed
the air, trying to catch the rabbit's scent once more.
Coyote smelled the rabbit again and became more
excited. Rabbits were her favorite food to eat. Her
heart jumped when she saw the rabbit in the distance.

| delicious: tasty |

Again, Coyote lowered herself close to the ground. She tried to be quiet as she crept closer. A light wind ruffled the rabbit's fur. The rabbit was looking away. It was busy eating a prickly pear fruit and did not seem to smell Coyote.

Coyote knew this would be a good time for a meal. She lifted her head and paid close attention to the wind's direction.

Aha! Coyote thought. *The wind is in my favor this morning. It's carrying my scent away from the rabbit. There's no way that rabbit can smell me!*

Coyote's stomach rumbled again. It was time to get something to eat.

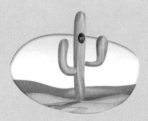

CHAPTER 3
The Hunt

Coyote crept closer and closer. She knew the rabbit could not see her. Her fur blended into the desert surroundings, helping her stay hidden. When she was a few feet away, Coyote ran as fast as she could toward the rabbit.

The **startled** rabbit ran away at top speed. Its long hind legs kicked up a big cloud of dust as it ran. This made it harder for Coyote to follow the rabbit. Coyote ducked as the brush poked at her nose. Thick dust choked her. The rabbit knew this game well.

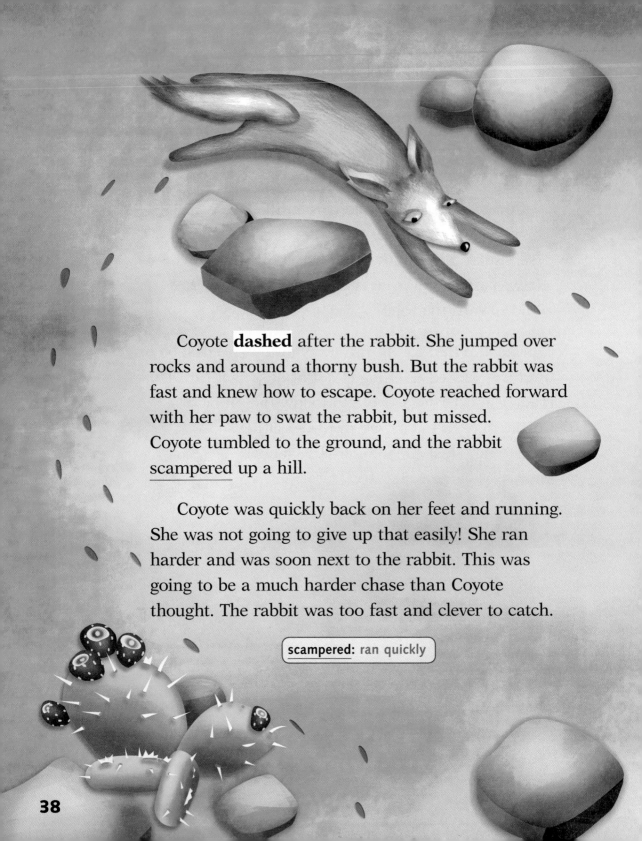

Coyote **dashed** after the rabbit. She jumped over rocks and around a thorny bush. But the rabbit was fast and knew how to escape. Coyote reached forward with her paw to swat the rabbit, but missed. Coyote tumbled to the ground, and the rabbit scampered up a hill.

Coyote was quickly back on her feet and running. She was not going to give up that easily! She ran harder and was soon next to the rabbit. This was going to be a much harder chase than Coyote thought. The rabbit was too fast and clever to catch.

scampered: ran quickly

I am very tired, Coyote thought. *I have to rest.* She lay down on the sand. Her belly rumbled, so Coyote dragged herself to her feet. Coyote knew that the rabbit was also tired and slowing down, so she ran toward the rabbit with one last burst of energy. The rabbit seemed to sense Coyote coming, so it changed directions, and Coyote crashed into a large rock! She fell to the ground and yelped. She was stunned for a moment and could not move. When she got up, the rabbit had **disappeared** into the desert.

stunned: surprised

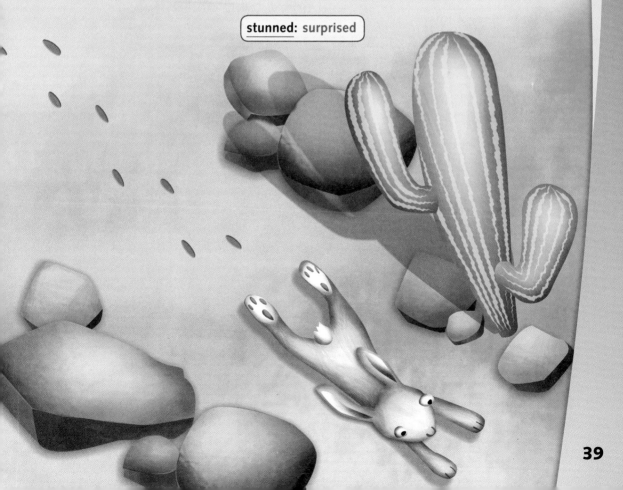

Coyote looked around and saw that the desert around her was suddenly quiet. The rabbit was gone, and Coyote's loud yelp had scared off all the other animals. Coyote would have to work even harder to find food.

A small cut on the bottom of Coyote's foot stung a little bit. Suddenly, she began to miss her mother very much. She remembered the den she was born in and how her mother used to bring her food to eat. But those days were gone, and now Coyote had to take care of herself.

She looked at her cut and then licked it. *It doesn't hurt too much*, she thought. *I think I'm ready to chase something else, but where will I find it?*

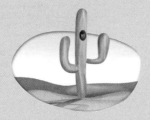

Stop and Think
Describe Coyote's experiences in the desert so far.

CHAPTER 4

Another Chance for a Meal

Coyote looked around and still did not see any animals. After all that work, her stomach was growling even louder.

She was a little sore from her fall, but otherwise she felt okay. She rested for a moment before heading toward the open desert outside of the canyon. *Food will be easier to find out here*, she thought. *There have to be some other animals somewhere*. She walked slowly until the pain in her foot began to go away.

GROWWWL

It was still early morning, and the sun was soft on the desert. People were walking and jogging up the road in the cool sunlight. Coyote had learned a long time ago to avoid humans, so she walked away from the road and tried to be very quiet. She stayed close to the creek that ran down from the mountains.

Then her stomach jumped when she smelled something good again. *Food!* Coyote caught the delicious scent of a mule deer as she left the

canyon behind her. She remembered what her mother had told her: Do not hunt mule deer until you are older. *Oh well*, she thought. *I am too hungry, so today I am going to try!*

Mule deer were very common in this part of the desert. Coyote knew they were fast runners and had a powerful kick. Only the largest and strongest coyotes would even try to chase them. But Coyote was tired of being hungry.

Strategy Tool Kit
Summarize

What does Coyote know about mule deer?

43

Three mule deer **does** stood in front of Coyote. They were eating desert plants and didn't seem to see her light fur against the desert background. Coyote tried to remember how her mother had hunted mule deer.

Coyote stalked the deer very slowly. She knew she was not as strong as they were, and she would have to try to get the smallest one away from the others. She was careful to stay behind a hill and out of the wind so that they would not catch her scent and run.

stalked: quietly hunted

As she got closer to the deer, Coyote smelled something new in the air. It was the scent of another coyote! She stopped and **crouched**. *Should I run away or continue to hunt?* she wondered. *Is the other coyote bigger and older?*

The other coyote smelled her too, and she came closer. "Who are you?" Coyote whispered.

The other coyote just looked at Coyote and blinked several times. "We'll talk later," the other coyote answered. "Follow me. Right now, we've got food to catch!"

Coyote was glad she finally had a hunting partner, even if the other coyote did not seem very friendly. It would be much easier to hunt the deer with another coyote, but it would still be very dangerous.

Together they circled the three deer. They were careful to be quiet, making sure they did not step on anything that would make noise.

Coyote noticed that one deer was smaller, and she knew this would be the one they would try to catch. The other deer would be too strong for even two coyotes to hunt.

She signaled to the other coyote that she was ready to spring on the three deer. Both coyotes ran forward as fast as they could, and the smaller deer was easily scared away from the others. They chased it, running closer and closer. Coyote crashed into a bush and fell, but then she got up and kept going.

Coyote barked with excitement. Maybe she would fill her empty belly after all!

signaled: made a sign

But neither coyote realized how **swift** and strong the deer was. Coyote's hunting partner raced out in front to cut off the deer's path. The deer stepped quickly in the other direction to <u>dodge</u> her, but Coyote was still chasing the deer from behind.

The deer kicked strongly with its hind legs and almost hit Coyote! Coyote lost her balance and tumbled to the ground with a yelp.

Then the deer kicked at Coyote's partner and barely missed her as well. She also lost her balance and tumbled to the ground. Plunk! She landed right next to Coyote. The deer turned back one more time before catching up with the other deer.

dodge: get away from

At least I am not the only clumsy coyote in the desert, Coyote thought. She tried not to smile as she turned and looked at her new hunting partner.

"That was close," Coyote sighed.

"Not close enough to catch a deer," the other coyote muttered, and then she stood up and looked away. "And I am tired of eating plants." She turned her back and walked toward a group of prickly plants.

"But I guess we have no choice," the other coyote said. "Follow me."

CHAPTER 5

A New Friend

Coyote sniffed around until she found another prickly pear. Her partner walked over to the plant with her. They frowned, took a bite of the fruit, and both of them winced at its sharp sting. This was not the food they had in mind. But the desert was starting to heat up, and there were no more animals around them.

The coyotes ate all the fruit they could find. It would be enough to fill their empty stomachs for now. Soon they would try again for a rabbit, some mice, or even a lizard.

winced: made a face

Both coyotes were tired from a day of hard work. The sun would soon go down, and they would try to hunt again in the dark.

"I do not think I'll be hunting deer for a while," Coyote said to her new friend. "It's too much work!"

"We will need to look for smaller animals next time," Coyote's friend agreed. "But thanks for the help. We'll have a better chance of getting some big prey when we are older."

Coyote inched backward to practice her jumping. "Hey," her friend warned. "Don't hurt yourself on that prickly pear. Let's go and find a new place to hunt tonight."

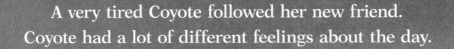

A very tired Coyote followed her new friend. Coyote had a lot of different feelings about the day.

Even though they had not caught anything to eat, Coyote was happy that she had found a friend. She looked out at the hot desert. She thought about how hard it had been to find food. She knew that both of them would have a better chance of surviving in the desert together.

Strategy Tool Kit
Make Inferences
Why would the coyotes have a better chance of surviving if they are together?

Coyote was grateful for the help, and for her
new friend. It was a good day in the desert
after all.

Think Back
Selection 2

A Check Understanding ★

List the animals and plants you read about in *Coyote's Desert Day*. Explain how these living things need each other. `PRACTICE COMPANION 126`

B Understand Literary Elements ★★

How was the setting important to this story? Discuss with your partner how the story might have been different if it had taken place in another ecosystem.

C Share and Compare ★★

Use your list of animals and plants from *Coyote's Desert Day* to explain food chains in the desert. Then compare the desert to your partner's ecosystem.

D Think Critically ★★★★

How are living things connected? Use examples from your selection to explain.

My Home Page

Selection Connection

You've learned about how living things need each other. What might happen if one of the living or nonliving things in an ecosystem changed?

★★★★
Show What You Know

Think about the following events: *pollution, flood,* and *children cleaning up a park.* How might each of these change an ecosystem?

Write about it.

PRACTICE COMPANION **127**

Preview ▶   online coach

What happens when there are changes to an ecosystem?
Preview pages 56–79. Then read *Spreading the Message* to find out.

SPREADING THE MESSAGE

by Laurel Haines ■ Illustrated by Deb Lucke

CHAPTER 1
MESSAGE IN A BOTTLE

Kwami stood on the dock, and the wind blew against his face. While looking out at Lake Michigan, he held the green plastic bottle and turned the cap tightly so that his message would stay dry.

When Kwami closed his eyes he saw the current carrying his bottle to faraway shores. *Maybe someone will find you in New York,* he thought, *or Louisiana, or maybe even Europe, or China, or . . .*

"Hurry up and throw that thing! I'm hungry!"

Kwami sighed. His twin sister, Tanesha, was the most **impatient** person he knew.

"I still don't get it," Tanesha said, shaking her head. "Why do you want to send a message in a bottle? You don't even know who might read it."

"Yes, Tanesha, that's the whole point," Kwami explained. "I get excited knowing that the water can take my message anywhere, to anyone."

Tanesha shrugged and asked, "Why don't you just send me an e-mail message? That way you'll be sure someone important will read it."

Kwami rolled his eyes. "You will never understand," he sighed as he lifted his arm and threw the bottle as far as he could into the lake.

explained: said

Strategy Tool Kit
Make Connections
What are some ways you send messages?

"Good throw, Kwami!" Mom shouted.

"The wind is really blowing," said Dad, "so I bet your bottle will travel far today."

"I hope so," Kwami said as he watched the bottle float away.

"Don't forget," Mom said. "We brought some wonderful food along with us. Let's quickly find a place where we can eat it."

Kwami and his family walked along the beach and were unhappy to see all of the litter on the sand.

"Well, we may have some trouble finding a clean spot," said Dad. "There's garbage everywhere."

Kwami saw something moving in a pile of trash. He and Tanesha walked closer to get a better look and were surprised to see a bird trapped in the litter. It struggled to free its foot from a plastic bag.

"That poor bird!" cried Tanesha.

They watched the bird twist until it finally freed itself and flew away.

Kwami was angry. "How can people throw their garbage on the beach? How can they not know how harmful it is to do that?" he shouted.

"There are garbage cans right there!" said Tanesha, equally upset.

Sadly, Kwami looked at the litter along the beach as far as he could see. He wanted to do something, but he just wasn't sure what.

equally: just as

Dad pointed to a pile of slimy garbage near the water's edge. "It's true that people can be **careless**," he said. "But this garbage might not come from people here on this beach. Some of this stuff could have been dumped miles and miles away. It could have floated here from a long way off, because you never can tell where the water will carry everything."

Kwami slowly sat on a log and thought about the message he had thrown into the lake. Suddenly, his bottle seemed exactly like all the other litter on the sand.

"What do you think will happen to my bottle?" he asked. "I must not have been thinking when I tossed it into the water. Was it a mistake to do that?"

"It's just one silly bottle," Tanesha said. "It won't **affect** anything."

Kwami tried to feel better but he couldn't stop thinking about his bottle. Was it any different from the rest of the garbage? Could it do any harm?

Strategy Tool Kit
Summarize
What did Kwami learn that made him worry about his bottle?

Kwami could not enjoy the lunch Mom and Dad had brought, even though it had a lot of his favorite foods. When he looked at the peanut butter sandwich wrapped in plastic, it reminded him of the poor bird that had been stuck in the plastic bag on the beach. The carrots that he always loved seemed like a pile of litter on his plate. The apple juice in his glass looked like dark and dirty water.

All he could think about was his message in the bottle. *My name is Kwami,* it said. *I love my beautiful beach, and I hope you love your beach too.* That was it, just a simple note to a stranger who might find it on the sand somewhere.

"Are you going to eat your carrots?" Tanesha asked. "If you're not, could I have them?"

Kwami sighed. "I'm just not hungry at all," he said. "You can take anything you want."

"Are you still thinking about that silly bottle?" Tanesha said. "It was just one little message, so it's not such a big deal. I just don't understand why you wanted to tell some stranger that you love the beach. Why should anyone care?"

"You're right," Kwami said to her. "You don't understand."

CHAPTER 2

A FRIGHTENING DISCOVERY

When they got home, Kwami and Dad looked up information on the Internet and learned about water pollution. They soon found an interesting Web site that explained how water currents could carry garbage far away.

"Listen to this," he called to Tanesha. "Animals and plants can use garbage like a raft. They can ride on bottles and cans."

Tanesha came over to look at a Web page that showed a picture of a tiny striped animal on a can. "That's neat," she said. "It's like a little **passenger**!"

"Maybe that's not so neat," Kwami said. "Keep reading. Some animals and plants are called **invasive** species. They cause trouble and upset the environment when they move from one ecosystem to another."

Kwami and Tanesha read about how invasive species could harm their new ecosystems. They learned that these species eat many animals and plants that are <u>native</u> to the ecosystem. They also learned how the invasive species could crowd out the native species by eating their food.

Kwami's heart sank. "So if an animal rides on my bottle, I cause even more problems than just litter. I may be helping to spread invasive species!"

He hoped that someone would find his bottle fast.

native: original

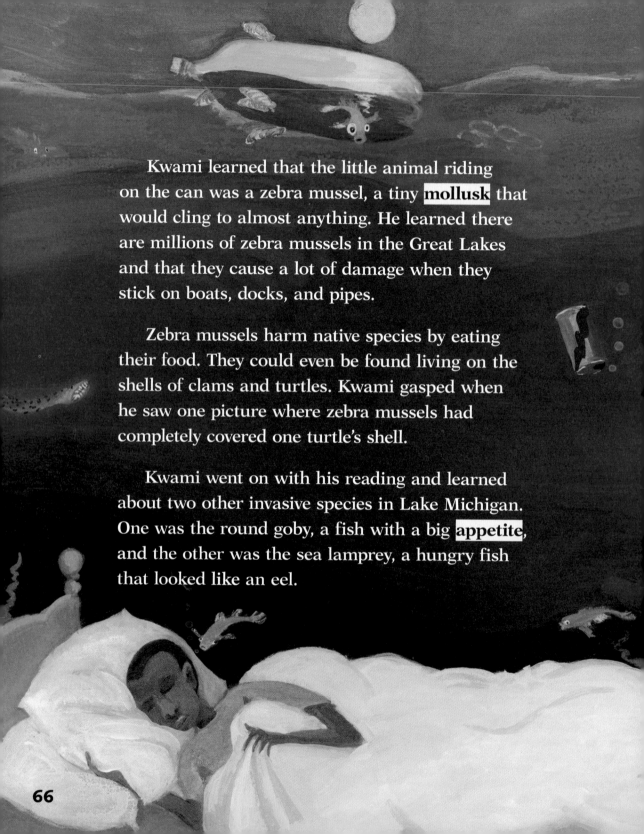

Kwami learned that the little animal riding on the can was a zebra mussel, a tiny **mollusk** that would cling to almost anything. He learned there are millions of zebra mussels in the Great Lakes and that they cause a lot of damage when they stick on boats, docks, and pipes.

Zebra mussels harm native species by eating their food. They could even be found living on the shells of clams and turtles. Kwami gasped when he saw one picture where zebra mussels had completely covered one turtle's shell.

Kwami went on with his reading and learned about two other invasive species in Lake Michigan. One was the round goby, a fish with a big **appetite**, and the other was the sea lamprey, a hungry fish that looked like an eel.

That night, Kwami dreamed that his bottle was filled and covered with invasive species! They were happily riding on the bottle, which was taking them to new lands. Kwami kept trying to grab the bottle, but the current kept pulling it away.

Kwami woke in a panic and thought, *I've got to do something about this. I can't keep having bad dreams like this!*

As he fell back asleep, he thought of a plan.

■

Stop and Think
In what ways does Kwami think his bottle could harm the environment?

CHAPTER 3

SOMEONE HAS TO DO IT

That morning, Kwami didn't **hesitate** as he quickly got dressed and rushed to the computer to print out some of the pictures he had seen.

At breakfast, Kwami told his plan to his family. "Someone has to clean up the lake. I can't do much by myself, but if I work with other people, maybe we can change things."

"Sure," said Tanesha, "but who wants to pick up all of that garbage?"

Kwami tried to feel **confident** and said, "I think I can get people interested."

That day he asked Mr. Morris, his teacher, if he could speak to the class. Kwami felt nervous, but he knew he could do it. He took a deep breath and walked to the front of the room.

"Summer is coming up, and we all love to go to the beach," he began. "But nobody likes it when the beach is dirty. Right now, the beach is really, really dirty."

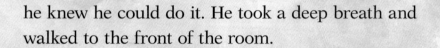

Kwami held up a picture of a bird standing in trash as he described what he had seen at the beach during his family's visit.

"Pollution is not just ugly," he warned the class. "It can harm plants and animals." Kwami held up a picture of a clam covered in zebra mussels and he explained what he had learned about invasive species. "We can make the beach clean and safe," he said, "if we take the time to remove the litter. That's why I'm starting a club to clean up the beach."

Kwami was surprised when he heard his classmates clapping. "That's a great idea, Kwami," said Mr. Morris. "Who wants to join this club?"

Kwami was surprised that Tanesha was the first to raise her hand.

At the first meeting, Kwami smiled as the room filled with classmates and friends.

Tanya looked sadly at the picture of the clam. "How can it eat when it is covered with zebra mussels?" she asked.

"It can't," Kwami answered. "It can't open its shell."

"Invasive species can cause a lot of harm to an ecosystem," said Mr. Morris. "Zebra mussels have few predators in the United States. Almost nothing can stop them."

"What can we do about it?" asked Marcus.

"We can start by getting rid of the garbage on the beach," said Kwami. "That way, the animals won't be able to ride to new places."

"You might also think about adopting the beach," said Mr. Morris. Everyone gave him a strange look.

"How can we adopt a beach?" asked Ashley. "We can't take it home with us, can we? My parents would scream if I brought all that sand into our house."

Mr. Morris laughed, and explained that adopting a beach meant promising to keep it clean.

"That's a great idea," said Kwami. "We need to keep cleaning the beach over and over again if we want it to stay beautiful."

Strategy Tool Kit
Summarize
What happened when Kwami told the class about his plan?

Tanesha looked at her brother and thought for a while. Suddenly she started to understand how much he loved the beach, and what he meant by his message in the bottle.

Mr. Morris noticed her staring into space. "Is there something that you want to say, Tanesha?" he asked.

"No," she answered. "I was just thinking about a talk I had with Kwami yesterday. I had no idea what he was speaking about then, but I think I understand him now."

She smiled as the club made a plan to visit the beach the next weekend. Mr. Morris said that he would <u>arrange</u> for a van to take them.

arrange: make plans

Early Saturday morning, the van pulled into the beach parking lot. When it stopped, Kwami and most of the others jumped out and started to run toward the beach. The sun was shining brightly in the sky, and the water looked beautiful beneath it.

"Wait, everybody!" called Mr. Morris. "I know that you all are excited, but you forgot your equipment!"

The kids turned around and ran back to Mr. Morris. He passed out big trash bags and thick rubber gloves.

equipment: supplies

"Remember," he said. "Be very careful. Wear gloves, and do not touch anything that's sharp."

"Those gloves are clunky," Ashley said. "Let's hurry up and clean the beach so we can take them off and run our fingers through the sand."

Everybody in the club put on gloves and ran toward the beach but Marcus stopped when he saw all the litter.

"This is going to take us all day!" he groaned.

"Then it's a good thing we got here so early," said Kwami cheerfully.

The students began picking up trash. "How did all this stuff get here?" Tanya wondered out loud as she bent down to pick up a plastic milk jug covered in slime. "It's gross."

"Just think about how nice the beach will look when the trash is gone," said Tanesha.

The group found different kinds of garbage on the beach such as balloons, toys, fast-food cartons, bottles, and cans.

As they worked, Mr. Morris and the children spoke to the people they saw and explained why they were cleaning up the beach. Most people thanked them and some people even helped pick up trash. By afternoon, the beach was clean.

"This is the last one," Kwami announced.

He bent over a bag filled with glass bottles. Kwami **plodded** over to the recycling bin and dumped it in.

Everyone cheered.

Mr. Morris smiled and spoke to everyone. "Your hard work has really made a difference. Let's thank Kwami for his wonderful idea."

Kwami looked at the clean beach. "Yes," he said. "We have done a lot."

Then his heart sank. "But my bottle is still out there."

■

Tanesha was standing at the water's edge when she shouted, "Kwami, come look at this!" Kwami ran to where his sister was standing and with his eyes, he followed her finger to what she was pointing at. There, bobbing in the water, was something green and shiny.

"That looks exactly like your bottle, right?" she asked him.

"But it can't be," he said.

A wave carried the object closer, until Kwami was able to reach out and grab it from the **surf**. Sure enough, it was the very bottle he had thrown into the lake just a week before.

"Look," he cried. "My message is still inside! And there's something else."

He turned the bottle to find that several zebra mussels were sitting on its smooth plastic surface.

"Sorry, boys," he said. "No more rides for you." Kwami pulled them off the bottle and then threw the bottle into a recycling bin.

"What about your message?" Tanesha teased him. "Don't you want someone to read it?"

Kwami grinned and said, "I'll send you an e-mail."

Tanesha smiled back at him. "I already know what the message says, and I agree with every word of it. I love our beautiful beach too."

■

Strategy Tool Kit
Make Connections
What are some things you can do to protect the ecosystems where you live?

Focus Question: What happens when there are changes to an ecosystem?

A Check Understanding ★

List the living things you read about in *Spreading the Message*. How did trash change the lake ecosystem for these living things? PRACTICE COMPANION 155

B Understand Literary Elements ★★

Who are the characters in *Spreading the Message*? What do the characters learn or realize by the end of the story? Talk it over with a partner.

C Share and Compare ★★

Summarize your story for a partner. Point out how the ecosystem in your story changed. Compare those changes to the changes in the ecosystem in your partner's story.

D Think Critically ★★★★

How are living things connected? Use examples from your selection to explain.

My Home Page

Think Ahead ▶
Selection 4

Focus Question: How do people play a part in ecosystems?

Selection Connection

You have learned what happens when there are changes to an ecosystem. What role do you think people can play in ecosystems?

Show What You Know

People's actions can affect ecosystems. Think about each of the following actions: *creating a man-made lake, going fishing,* and *planting a tree.* What effect could each action have?

Write about your ideas.

PRACTICE COMPANION **156**

Preview ▶

online coach

How do people play a part in ecosystems? Preview pages 82–102. Then read *Ecosystem Invaders* to find out.

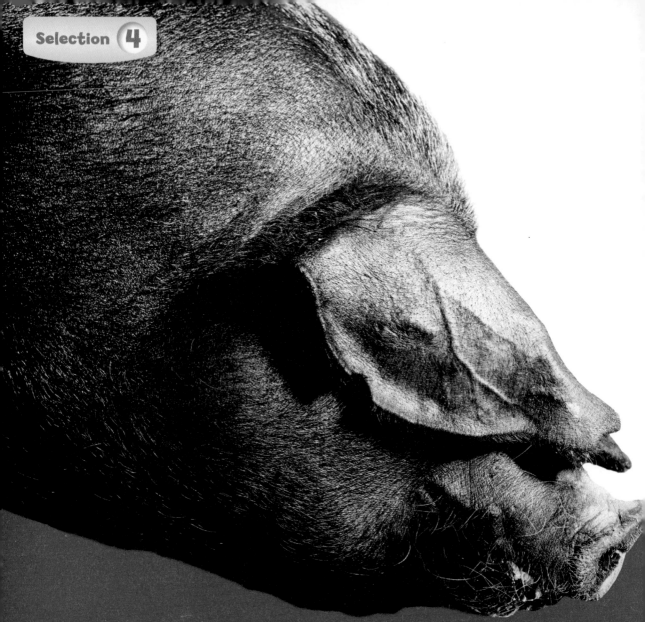

Ecosystem
INVADERS

by Katie Sharp

Upsetting the Balance

Picture a peaceful stream. Some plants grow on the land along its edges, while others grow right in the water. Frogs hop from rock to rock. Some fish lay eggs, and **reptiles** doze in mud. Bears splash in the stream as deer nibble at flowers on the shore. A hawk swoops down from the sky to grab a mouse.

The stream you are picturing is a healthy ecosystem. It has a balance of living and nonliving things. It has many healthy food chains.

Now picture an animal from a different ecosystem moving to this stream. You may not be able to tell where the animal comes from, but you know it does not belong there! This new animal has no competition for food. It causes many problems.

A turtle pops up for a breath in this healthy stream.

Food Chain for a Stream

Every plant and animal in a food chain is important. Below are some plants and animals you might find near a stream. How do you think each plant and animal is connected? What do you think would happen if all the mayflies disappeared?

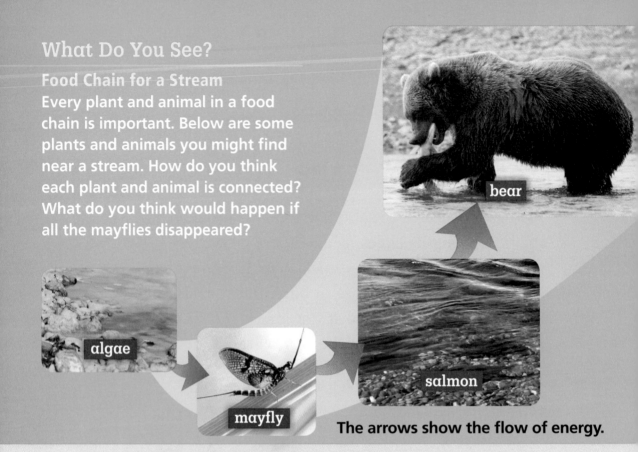

The arrows show the flow of energy.

The new animal is an invader, a living thing that has moved somewhere it may not belong. It destroys the places where frogs hunt, lizards sleep, and fish lay eggs. More plants and animals die than normal. The new animal **disrupts** the food chains. This animal is an invasive species. The native species do not have adaptations to compete with it or fight it.

In most cases, people bring an invasive species to a new ecosystem. This is often by accident. The invasive species slips into its new home without anyone noticing.

Sometimes people do not know the harm a species can cause. They decide to bring it somewhere new. After all, a plant or animal in its natural ecosystem does not hurt the place where it lives. The trouble starts when a species moves into an ecosystem where it does not belong.

What problems do you think invasive species can cause? Let's learn about four of them to find out.

zebra mussels

brown tree snake

feral pigs

kudzu

Strategy Tool Kit
Ask and Answer Questions
How might an invasive species get to a new ecosystem? Use the text to help you find the answer.

85

2

Zebra Mussels
Flex Their Muscle

The zebra mussel is a freshwater animal. It gets its name from the dark and light stripes on its shell, which remind some people of a zebra. Zebra mussels are very small. Most are about the size of the nail on your finger. But do not let the size fool you. This little mussel can cause big trouble!

Zebra mussels are attached to this captain's wheel underwater.

This animal first lived only in the Caspian and Black Seas in Europe and Asia. In 1988 scientists were **confused** when they found zebra mussels in Lake Saint Clair in the United States. Nobody had ever seen zebra mussels there before.

The scientists learned that ships had brought the striped invaders to the lake. The zebra mussels had been living in water in the ships. Some of this water spilled into the lake, and the zebra mussels were released. The animals soon spread to other places.

released: let go

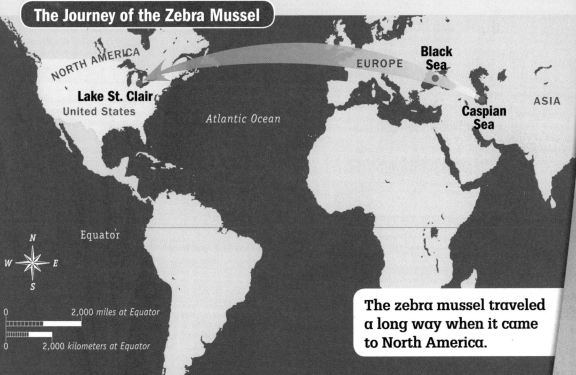

The Journey of the Zebra Mussel

NORTH AMERICA

EUROPE

Black Sea

Lake St. Clair
United States

Atlantic Ocean

Caspian Sea

ASIA

N
W ✦ E
S

Equator

0   2,000 *miles at Equator*

0   2,000 *kilometers at Equator*

The zebra mussel traveled a long way when it came to North America.

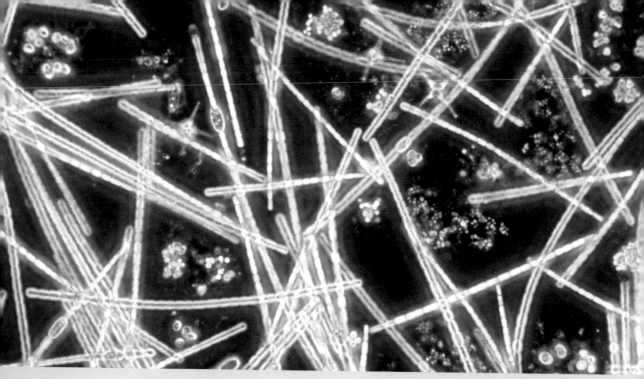

This picture of plankton was taken through a microscope.

How did these tiny invaders spread so fast? A female zebra mussel makes millions of eggs. The eggs hatch quickly, and the young drift in the water. They stick to anything solid and do not let go. They cling to boats, turtles, crayfish, and other mollusks. The mussels move with these things and spread quickly.

Zebra mussels damage an ecosystem because they eat so much. They eat tiny water plants called plankton. Native species also eat plankton. The native species starve when the zebra mussels eat so much of their food source.

starve: go hungry

Zebra mussels also cling to native mussels and clams. What happens? Soon the native animals cannot open their shells. They cannot eat or breathe. These native animals die and then other animals no longer have food.

So how can the invaders be stopped? People who use boats can help stop zebra mussels from spreading. They can clean their boats carefully before they move them to a new lake or stream.

Large amounts of zebra mussels have attached themselves to the bottom of this boat.

Feral Pigs:
Good Pigs Gone Bad

The feral, or wild, pig is a real pig! But it's not like the tame animals you can find on farms. This invasive species comes to an ecosystem and makes a big mess.

Feral pigs first lived in Europe and Asia. Spanish explorer Hernando de Soto brought pigs to North America in 1539. Many farmers let their pigs run free in those days. Some of the pigs ran away to live in the wild.

Hernando de Soto explored the area that is today the southeastern United States.

Years later, hunters brought a pig called the Eurasian wild boar to North America. The people who brought these pigs thought it might be fun to let them go free, and then hunt them.

The feral pigs in the United States today are a mix of de Soto's animals and the Eurasian wild boars. They are an invasive species in more than twenty states. California has the highest number of feral pigs in the United States.

wild boar

A World of Words

What on Earth Does *Feral* Mean? *Feral* is a word that comes from Latin. The Latin word *ferus* means "wild," so *feral* means "wild" or "like a wild beast." A *feral* pig is a wild pig. Other words from *ferus* that might make you think of wild animals are *fierce* and *ferocious.*

Feral pigs will look almost anywhere for food.

It should be no surprise to you that feral pigs behave like . . . pigs! They love to eat and dig. They destroy plants when they root around for food. Feral pigs gobble eggs and small animals. They **ruin** streams and ponds. They disrupt ecosystems at every level.

Native species are helpless against the feral pig. Feral pigs destroy their ecosystems and eat up almost everything in their path. Plants and animals cannot grow back fast enough.

Many feral pigs also carry **diseases**. These diseases can spread to other animals and even people. Feral pigs can also make life hard for farmers. How do you think they harm farmers? The pigs destroy crops and kill farm animals.

The feral pig has few natural predators except people. The only way to get rid of these wild animals is by hunting or trapping them. But it's nearly impossible to get them all, so the invaders are here to stay.

Dogs are sometimes used to hunt feral pigs.

Stop and Think
How do the invasive species you've read about upset the balance of the ecosystems?

Sneaky Snakes

The brown tree snake first lived only in Australia and some of its surrounding islands. There is little food in these places. The **shortage** of food keeps the population of snakes under control. That helps keep them from doing harm to their home ecosystems.

In the late 1940s the brown tree snake came to Guam, where it caused a lot of trouble. This small island in the Pacific Ocean is about six thousand miles west of San Francisco.

Guam

PACIFIC ISLANDS

Pacific Ocean

N
W   E
S

0   500   1,000 Miles
0   500   1,000   1,500 Kilometers

AUSTRALIA

Guam is so small that it doesn't appear on many maps.

A brown tree snake sticks out its long tongue.

Brown tree snakes live in trees and other places, such as logs and caves. They can go a long time without food. This is why the snakes could live through the journey to Guam.

People did not know they were bringing brown tree snakes to Guam. The snakes hid like stowaways in ships. Once the snakes invaded the island, they started eating birds and other small animals.

The native species on Guam were not able to protect themselves from the brown tree snakes. Nature had not given these species anything they could use to fight off the new hunters. To make matters even worse, the snakes had no predators. No other animals could **compete** with them for food, so they quickly spread.

The Guam rail, a species native to Guam, cannot fly, so it is easy prey for snakes. The Guam rail is about 11 inches tall.

brown tree snake

Today brown tree snakes are **devouring** many other animals on the island. Some native birds no longer live on the island. Other animals are also leaving. These losses upset the ecosystem.

Brown tree snakes can hide almost anywhere. Planes or ships in Guam are searched. People set traps for them. But stopping the brown tree snake is not easy. Unfortunately, these snakes have made themselves at home on the island.

Strategy Tool Kit
Ask and Answer Questions
Why was the brown tree snake able to take over the island of Guam? Use the text to help you find the answer.

A Beautiful Invader

Believe it or not, some pretty plants can also be invasive species!

In 1876 the United States turned one hundred years old, and Americans decided to hold a big party in Philadelphia. Many countries built fancy <u>exhibits</u> for this huge party.

The Japanese made a garden filled with lots of interesting plants. A beautiful vine called kudzu was in the garden. American gardeners saw this plant and wanted to grow it in their gardens.

> exhibits: displays

Philadelphia Centennial Exposition, 1876

Kudzu coats almost everything around it.

Its large leaves were shaped something like hearts, and its **fragrant** purple flowers smelled really good. Soon these happy Americans began to plant this ornamental vine in their gardens.

Farmers grew kudzu and sold it. Other people planted the vine on hills and near water. They used kudzu to keep soil from washing away.

It's too bad no one guessed that this plant would be so hard to control!

ornamental: decorative

Kudzu can even cover an entire house!

Amazing Facts

Big and Fast

The roots of a kudzu plant can weigh more than 300 pounds. And don't stand too close, kudzu grows up to one foot per day.

Kudzu winds and creeps everywhere it grows. Like a pretty, leafy bandage, it covers almost everything. The vine is mostly a problem in the southern United States. There, the climate is good for the plant. The summers there are hot and rainy. It's just the kind of climate that kudzu loves!

As kudzu grows and grows, it harms or kills other plants that get in its way. Kudzu vines can form a thick coat on trees, blocking sunlight. Without sunlight, the trees die.

People have tried to use poison to kill kudzu. They have let farm animals eat it. But even when people think that kudzu is gone, it may not be. Its seeds can stay alive without growing for several years, so it can grow back suddenly even after its leaves have disappeared. Like other invasive species, kudzu is hard to stop.

Strategy Tool Kit
Determine Important Information
What is the most important thing you learned about kudzu? What details are interesting but not that important?

A Delicate Balance

Zebra mussels, feral pigs, brown tree snakes, and kudzu are important parts of the food chains in their home habitats. They do not cause problems in their native ecosystems. But when they move somewhere else, they can harm the living things there. They can upset the balance of an ecosystem and become an invasive species.

There are many other kinds of invasive species besides those four. People must do their best to be aware of the effect a new species can have on an ecosystem. That new species could make trouble by destroying the **delicate** balance of life.

There is lots of life in a healthy ecosystem.

Focus Question: How do people play a part in ecosystems?

A **Check Understanding** ★

Think about the roles people played in the ecosystems you read about. In what ways did people help or harm the ecosystem? Create a T-chart to show the roles people played. PRACTICE COMPANION 175

B **Understand Text Features** ★★

Sidebars are sometimes used in nonfiction texts to give us more information about a topic or to tell us interesting facts. Find a sidebar in your text and read it to a partner. Why might the author have included it?

C **Share and Compare** ★★

Summarize your selection. Use your T-chart to explain the role that people played in your ecosystem. Explain your chart to a partner. Are the roles people played similar to or different from those in your partner's selection?

D **Think Critically** ★★★★

How are living things connected? Use examples from the selection to explain.

My Home Page

How are living things connected?

Use these activities to show what you've learned about the theme question.

Design and Create

1. Design your own ecosystem. Draw a habitat, living things, and nonliving things.

2. Next label the producers and consumers. Label the herbivores and carnivores.

3. Then write a paragraph explaining the connections between all the parts of your ecosystem.

Multimedia

1. Create a radio or TV announcement telling your community how to protect your ecosystem.

2. Present your project to the class.

★★★★

Book Club

1. Choose your favorite selection from the unit. Tell your group why you chose it.

2. Read your favorite part aloud.

3. Search for other books on ecosystems to read and share.

Be an Author

1. Think about what happens if you remove part of an ecosystem.

2. Use your thoughts to write a story about an ecosystem that has a missing piece.

3. Read your story to a friend.

Glossary

Pronunciation Key

a	bat	oi	toy
ā	ape	ou	shout
air	**air**	ŏŏ	book
ä	p**ar**k	ōō	moon
e	let	s	sun
ē	**ea**sy	sh	pressure
i	if	th	**the, thing**
ī	lie	u	nut
îr	dear	ûr	circle
k	cause	ə	ago
o	lot	ər	mother
ō	go	′	primary stress
ô	all	′	secondary stress

absorb (ab sôrb′) *v.* to soak up, as in liquid, or take in;
The paper towels absorb the spilled water. **16**

affect (ə fekt′) *v.* to influence or change;
Two dry months will affect the amount of water in the river. **61**

appetite (a′ pi tūt′) *n.* the desire, or want, for food;
We feed our puppy a whole can of food because she has a big appetite. **66**

bloom (blōōm)
v. to have or produce flowers; to shine out;
Daffodils bloom early in the spring. **26**

canopy (ka′ nə pē) *n.* a covering hanging over another object; the upper branchy layer of a forest;
The tree branches formed a canopy to shade the forest. **12**

careless (kair′ ləs) *adj.* not paying attention or taking care;
The careless driver crashed into the mailbox. **60**

clumsy (klum′ zē) *adj.* not graceful; uneasy and awkward;
My clumsy cousin is always dropping things. **31**

compete (kəm pēt′) *v.* to be in a state of rivalry;
The teams compete to win the game. **96**

confident (kon′ fi dənt) *adj.* trusting in yourself or someone else; being sure;
We are confident that our coach is training us correctly. **68**

confuse (kən fyo͞oz′) *v.* to mix up;
We wore masks to confuse everyone at
the party. **87**

crouch (krouch) *v.* to move close to
the ground, with knees bent;
I will crouch down and hide behind
the bush. **45**

dash (dash)
v. to move
quickly;
A lizard can dash
from place to
place in the blink of an eye. **38**

delicate (de′ li kət) *adj.* fragile; easily
upset or broken;
Please be careful with those delicate
glasses. **102**

devour (di vour′) *v.* to eat; to use up;
An owl can devour a mouse
quickly. **97**

disappear (dis′ ə pîr′) *v.* to pass
from view;
The sun made the water on the
sidewalk disappear. **39**

disease (di zēz′) *n.* a sickness or
illness in a living thing;
The plant's disease made the leaves
yellow. **93**

disrupt (dis rupt′) *v.* to break apart
or stop;
The parrot's loud cries always disrupt
my nap. **84**

distinct (di stingkt′) *adj.* different,
not the same;
Every flower has its own distinct
smell. **12**

doe (dō) *n.* the adult female of
mammals, such as deer, rabbits, and
kangaroos;
The doe protected her fawn. **44**

ecosystem
(ē′ kō sis′ təm)
n. a community of
living and nonliving
things that interact
with each other;

Fish, whales, and seaweed are all part
of the ocean ecosystem. **4**

fragrant (frā′ grənt)
adj. having a
pleasing smell;
The garden is filled
with fragrant
flowers. **99**

hesitate (he′zə tāt) *v.* to hold back because of feeling unsure;
If the players hesitate, they will lose the chance to score the point. **68**

impatient (im′ pā′ shənt) *adj.* restless; not calm;
My impatient brother could hardly wait for the movie to start. **57**

interdependence (in′ tər di pen′ dəns) *n.* when two or more people or things depend upon each other;
The interdependence of humans and plants is very strong. **8**

invasive (in vā′ siv) *adj.* tending to spread;
Kudzu is an invasive plant that covers everything around it. **64**

moist (moist) *adj.* damp; slightly wet;
My bath towel is moist. **11**

mollusk (mo ləsk′) *n.* an animal with a soft body and shell, such as a snail or a clam;
The girls studied the shell of the mollusk that lay on the shore. **66**

monsoon (mon sōōn′) *n.* the heavy ocean winds that bring heavy rain, especially in the Indian Ocean;
Last year's monsoon destroyed the seaside villages. **34**

passenger (pa′ sən jər) *n.* a traveler in a car, train, or other form of transportation;
One passenger boarded the plane late. **64**

plod (plod) *v.* to walk heavily or slowly;
The boys plod through the deep snow. **77**

precipitation (pri si′ pə tā′ shən) *n.* condensation from vapor that falls as rain or snow;

The rain forest receives a lot of precipitation. **8**

reptile (rep′ tīl) *n.* a cold-blooded animal that moves on its belly and has scales, such as an alligator or a crocodile;
The boy dreamt of seeing a live reptile. **83**

ruin (rōō′ ən) *v.* to damage greatly;
Hail can ruin a farmer's crops. **92**

shortage (shôr′ tij) *n.* not enough of something;
There was a shortage of gasoline. **94**

startled (stär′ təld) *adj.* shocked or surprised;
The animal looked startled after the thunder banged. **37**

stumble (stum′ bəl) *v.* to trip or to walk unsteadily;
You might stumble when you walk on that rocky road. **31**

surf (sûrf) *n.* the splash of sea waves on the shore;
We played in the surf at the edge of the beach. **78**

survive (sər vīv′) *v.* to remain alive;
The animals cannot survive without food and water. **8**

swift (swift) *adj.* able to move quickly;
His swift horse won the race. **48**

terrific (tə ri′ fik) *adj.* wonderful or very good;
My mom makes terrific pizza. **23**

transform (trans fôrm′) *v.* to change in appearance, shape, or character;
That caterpillar will transform and become a butterfly. **24**

Index

Acknowledgments

Photo Credits: Cover ©Pete Oxford/Minden Pictures; **4-5** Photodisc/Getty Images; **5** (bl) Bruno Morandi/Getty Images; **6** ©Pete Oxford/Minden Pictures; **7** (t) ©Natural Visions/Alamy, (b) ©Banana Pancake/Alamy; **8** ©John Warburton-Lee/Danita Delmont.com; **10** ©Marc Anderson/ Acclaim Images, (t) ©AGE Fotostock/SuperStock; **12-13** ©Greenshoots Communications/Alamy; **14** ©Jacques Jangoux/Photo Researchers. Inc; **15** (l) ©Medio Images/PunchStock, (l) ©Age Fotostock/ SuperStock, (l) ©Pete Oxford/Naturepl.com, (tl) ©Dr. Morley Read/Shutterstock, (tc) ©Photo By Bob Richard, APHIS/USDA, (tc) ©Medio Images/SuperStock; **16** (t) ©David Allan Brandt/Stone/ Getty Images, (b) ©Kevin Schafer/Alamy; **17** ©Brand X Pictures/Getty Images; **18** ©David Tipling/ Alamy; **19** ©Tom Brakefield/Getty Images; **20** (c) ©Terry Whittaker/Alamy, (l) ©Bjanka Kadic/ Alamy; **21** ©Creatas/PunchStock; **22** Photodisc/Getty Images; **23** (t) ©Tui De Toy/Minden PIctures/National Geographic Stock; **24** (t) ©Michael & Patricia Fogden/Corbis, (b) Geostock/ Getty Images; **25** ©Hans&Judy Beste/Lockman Transparencies; **26** ©Ian Shive/Aurora/Getty Images; **27** ©Digital Vision/Getty Images; **28** ©Creatas/PunchStock; **29** (c) Photos.com/Jupiter Images, (b) ©Christian Musat/Shutterstock; **55** (c) ©Creatas/Punchstock, (r) ©Digital Vision/ PunchStock; **81** (c) ©Digital Vision/Getty Images, (r) ©Ian Shive/Getty Images; **82** ©Dan Burn-Forti/Photographers Choice/Getty Images; **83** ©Timothy Laman/National Geographic/Getty Images; **84** (bl) ©Jerry Driendi/Photographer's Choice/Getty Images, (bc) ©Thomas Dobner 2006/ Alamy, (br) ©Malcolm Schuyl/Alamy, (tr) ©David tipling / Alamy; **85** (tl) ©Ed Reschke / Peter Arnold Inc., (tr) ©James Balog/Stone/Getty Images, (bl) ©Roger Bamber/Alamy, (br) ©Bruce Coleman Inc./Alamy; **86** ©Stock Up Images/Alamy; **88** ©M.I Walker/Photo Researchers, Inc.; **89** ©Ottmar Bierwagen/Photographers Direct, (inset) ©Ottmar Bierwagen/Photographers Direct; **90** ©The Granger Collection, New York; **91** ©Tariq Dajani/Photonica/Getty Images; **92** ©David Hosking/Alamy; **93** ©Chip Simons; **94** (t) ©James Balog/Stone/Getty Images; **95** ©Theo Allofs/The Image Bank/Getty Images; **96** ©G. Ronald Austing/Photo Researchers; **97** ©Michael McCoy/Photo Researchers, Inc.; **98** ©The Print Collector/Alamy; **99** ©David R. Frazier Photolibrary, Inc./Alamy; **100** ©Bruce Coleman Inc./Alamy; **102** ©Creatas Images/Alamy; **103** ©Stock-Up Images/Alamy.

Art Credits: 11 ©The McGraw-Hill Companies, Inc.; **30-44** ©The McGraw-Hill Companies, Inc./ Linda Oliver; **56-79** ©The McGraw-Hill Companies, Inc./Deb Lucke; **87** ©McGraw-HIll Companies, Inc.; **94** ©The McGraw-Hill Companies, Inc.